Shabnam's Day Out

JOAN SOLOMON

Photographs by
Joan Solomon &
Ryan Solomon

HAMISH HAMILTON
London

Whenever Shabnam goes out with her family
she gets lost.
Today they're at St Katherine docks
and she's lost again.

"Nawaz!
        Riaz!
              Saiqa!
                    Zaid!"
she calls
to her brothers
and sisters.
Can't any of them
hear her?

Riaz hears her.
"Shabnam's lost again,"
he thinks.
"I'll fetch her, but
Nawaz must look after her.
I did last time."

"I saw the grey pigeon that eats in our playground," Shabnam tells her brother Nawaz.
"I said hello and he flew away.
You all went away too."
"Don't be silly. It wasn't the same pigeon," says Nawaz.
"Now stay here Shabs.
It's my turn to climb on that wheel."

But Shabnam is off again exploring.
This time Mum fetches her.
"Come on let's go and look at the water.
You'll get lost if you go off alone."
"Can we get on a boat Mum?"
"Where do you want to go Shabnam?"
Zaid asks her. Zaid is happy just looking
at the water. So are Mummy and Daddy.

Saiqa likes sitting on the capstan. It's warm
and just right for swinging your legs.
She watches her brothers pick leaves
and sings to herself, keeping time
with her legs:

> I wonder what the boys are doing,
> The boys are doing,
> The boys are doing,
> I wonder what the boys are doing,
> Doing over there?

> "I'll go and have a look."

Riaz and Nawaz are racing boats
made from the leaves they have picked
Saiqa would like to race one too.

But Dad thinks it's time for lunch.
"Come," he says to Mum "let's go and eat."

"We'll have to stop now," says Riaz walking away.
"Dad's calling. He's over at the car already."

"I want to go home," says Shabnam.
She is hungry and thirsty.
"Be patient Shabs," says Dad,
"and we'll have our lunch
in the park."

In the park it's noisy
running through the dry leaves.
"This is better than racing those boats,"
calls Saiqa who didn't have
a chance to make her boat.
Mum, Dad and Zaid have found
a picnic spot by the time Saiqa
reaches them.

Corn-on-the-cob is everyone's favourite.
Especially the hot corn you buy outside the park.
"It's very greasy," says Zaid.

"It's nice," says Shabnam,
who loves sucking the butter
that's soaked into the cob.
But really she's eating as fast as she can
because she knows there are some swings over there.

"This is bigger than the see-saw in our park," says Saiqa. "There's more space here for Shabs and me," says Riaz, "go and sit at your end Saiqa."

"This roundabout's better too," says Saiqa.
But Shabnam thinks the swing is best of all.
The only trouble is that as soon as
she starts swinging she hears her mother call.

It's time to leave and meet Dad at the Mosque. Dad prays five times every day and today he's gone to the big Mosque in Regents Park.

It's a beatiful Mosque with a golden dome
where Muslim men quietly stand and say their
prayers. Sometimes they kneel right down
on special prayer rugs.

Before going in, everyone
has to take off his shoes.
That man praying alone
isn't Saiqa's father.
Her Dad must be down
in the front with
all the others.

Anyway Saiqa must wait
till he comes.
Girls aren't allowed to go
where the men pray.
She's worried that she'll
be late for her prayer class.
Her teacher, the Mohvey,
gets cross if you're late.

Saiqa is a bit late for her class.
"Where are you up to, Yasmin," she asks her
friend, trying to find the place.

She is in time to read the Koran,
the Muslim Holy Book, with her group
and reading to the Mohvey is the main part.

This Mohvey's very strict about the way
they make their Arabic sounds. They
have to be just right.

Shabnam doesn't mind that. She likes the prayer school. Her friends are there and that's the one place she doesn't get lost.

We should like to thank the Sharif family
for their hospitality and help and for
taking part in this book.
We should also like to thank Laila Lelane
for her help and advice.

Copyright © 1980 Joan Solomon
Photographs © 1980 Joan Solomon and Ryan Solomon
All rights reserved
First published in Great Britain 1980 by
Hamish Hamilton Children's Books Ltd,
Garden House, 57–59 Long Acre, London WC2E 9 JZ

Printed in Great Britain by
Fakenham Press Limited,
Fakenham, Norfolk

British Library Cataloguing in Publication Data

Solomon, Joan
    Shabnam's day out.
    I. Title
    823'.9'1J   PZ7.S696

ISBN 0-241-10420-3